MW00611485

This journal belongs to

_____

Introduction

This journal is intended to help you better connect with your higher self, the spiritual, true and timeless you. And to remind you that you are much more than this physical existence. It is my belief that you are a multidimensional being, full of life, light and creativity. The same life force that flows through you flows through all of creation. Therefore, you are one with all of life and never alone. In these pages, you will find a safe and quiet space to rest, where you can put aside your worries and concerns and express and explore your innermost feelings, hopes and dreams. May these pages become your sacred space, a place of peace where you can listen to the voice of your soul and express all the colour and light in your heart.

With love and light,
Toni

I

the artist

poet and dreamer

inside you

you

the image

the poem,

and dream

inside me

the dreamer

and the dreamed

are one

and together we shall create

We travel the endless corridors of the mind,
until one day, we find a pathway that leads to the heart.

Nothing will change the oneness that is.
Go forth and be true to yourself and others

dare to be different
to make mistakes
create, for it is in creation
that you exist

your whole life is a creation
in this world full of dreams
...full of life

deep within I have always felt your presence
though I did not know who you were, nor your name,
I felt your warmth and love

so comforting you made me feel less lonely
and a little less fearful as you shed light
on the shadows I imagined around me

deep within I have always felt the soul of the earth also
as I unknowingly tuned into the oneness

strangely, I also sensed a kind of cosmic belonging
even though I felt out of place in my immediate surroundings

… these thoughts lead me back in time to the child I once was
and perhaps, in essence, still am

If I could talk to you, I would tell you not to worry.
I would tell you that you are beautiful even though you do not know it.
I would tell you I love you and you are perfect just as you are.
I would tell you to reach for the stars, not so much the ones in the sky,
but those glowing brightly within you, just behind your doubt and insecurities.

I would tell you to be sincere and kind to everyone, especially to yourself.

I would tell you to be grateful for this life.
I would tell you that when you are in pain or are suffering
To remember that things will get better

I would try to tell you a million things but, mostly, I would hug you and say
I love you.

in oneness, we all exist
through love and hate
pleasure and pain,
joy and sadness

go now
step into the void of uncertainty
trust in life, in existence, in soul,
trust that the angels will guide you
will share each experience with you,
and most importantly, always love you

when a storm flows into your life
remember, it's just passing by, all will pass,
life is in perpetual movement
there is peace always in your higher mind and spirit,
let there also be peace in your heart

Prayers and Reflections

your great dreamy ocean fills my heart with love and gratitude
i am blessed by your existence — blue sphere of dreams —
gaia, mother, goddess

you who smiles, weeps and whispers with a gentle breeze
to remind me of the seed in my heart, the gift of creativity

i feel your presence everywhere in everything
as i look to the sky through clouds of memory
the sun is so full of warmth

this earth you dreamed into being
this world still evolving in your emerald heart

the light of future stars, new beginnings and endings
magical imaginings and blessings

as we evolve with you, mother goddess,
creator of trees and mountains, rivers and soil, air and oceans

nourished and intuitively guided by your timeless wisdom and compassion
you now call us to unite and move past our illusions,
to leave behind all we think we know, if only for a while,
and step into the light of a divine heart, so full of stars

for at best, what we know
is but a particle of truth
within a far greater truth

let us first agree that we do not have to agree,
or see the world in the same way,
or hold the same beliefs

indeed, that is impossible and an unwise goal
for we are each a unique part of the one
with our own perspective, flavour and gifts

let us unite through love,
leave our thoughts behind
as we enter her heart and breathe her wisdom
and compassion

let us be silent, so nothing is lost in translation

for the language of love is universal
and in essence, we are already one

let us be still and connect
with one another and gaia

let us form a stream of light that flows to and from
her dreamy ocean, in and out of our hearts, as we breathe her love
let us be of service to her, and one another
let us be kind

there is nothing more to understand, explain or make sense of

just feel the presence of the one who holds the dreamy ocean in her heart
and the sun, moon and stars in her eyes
and her light will brighten even our darkest hour

namaste

Things will be as they always have been
The world shall continue as it has always done
All comes and goes and comes again
This is the way of the world...

Infinite creativity and possibility
expressed through us, lived and experienced by us,
in a universe that gives space to our dreams and desires.
Life everlasting moves us onward through the circle of life, forever repeating,
while giving the impression that we travel this road for the very first time.

Deep within the human heart and mind,
there is the infinite space of God, Goddess, Angels

I flow through the invisible
formless fibres of your imagination
I feel you, I see your hopes and dreams,
the colours inside you, the earth, the sky, the stars shining inside you,
I see you collecting images like shells, upon the shore
from the great the ocean of existence inside you

Peace

You shall not find me while trying to make sense of this world

nor at times when you are fearful,

for it is difficult for my light to enter the world of thought.

Come, rest awhile with me in the shadows,

allow silence to be your voice,

all that is unspoken shall ignite a flame in your heart.

There are infinite space and light within every atom of you,

And so it is that you cannot lose me nor I, lose you.

time goes by without a trace
except for the love you keep in your heart

There will come a time when all you feel is gratitude.

have the courage
to follow your dream
to listen to your heart
to go forth and shine your light

Earth Song

Of time and space
and all that is spaceless

Of trees glowing
in my heart
and wildflowers

spreading through vast green
yellow fields
and spaces

Of seasons past
and those yet to come

Of oceans
unfolding
memories

and the gentle breeze

that blows
softly
caressingly

surrounding
embracing
recollecting

gathering
fading
into yesterdays light

Of this all-absorbing life
and dream
and death
and of coming
and going
and of all things eternal
like the soul

Of atoms of energy
flowing through the vast spaceless space
of infinity
and the earth beneath my feet
the stars in your eyes
and moss
and leaves of the forest

and love...

In the stillness of your heart, a treasure awaits.

Life is made of big and little things.
One day you will look back and smile,
knowing how precious every moment was.

I, Creativity, am living energy.
I manifest instantly, spontaneously when the mind is clear.
I can be channelled but not contained.
I bridge worlds, dimensions and realities.
Your heart is my canvas.
Together we shall
paint the sky,
collide in music,
fall into poems.

be courageous, express yourself freely without censorship
you will discover that you are far more than you have imagined

The one thing that

we all have in common

is that we are different

but only slightly different

for we are part of the same tapestry.

There are over seven-billion truths in the world today

and every day new truths are born

because every one of us is part of the truth

each with their own piece of truth

no one person holds all the truth

that is why we can never agree on anything

until we join together and agree that it's alright to disagree

Both the past and the future are held in this present moment.

Life is circular.
There are no beginnings or ends,
just different stages of a journey.

Life has given you wings of awareness
to explore endless dimensions of creativity.
You can imagine and build your future.
Write your own story,
but be mindful, be grateful for all blessings you receive,
and always remember, life is your co-creator.

there are so many doors
old and new
made of stone, metal, crystal, wood

open any door
and reconnect
with a part of you
you may have forgotten

you may find yourself
drawn into a crystal world
where angels greet you
in a language strangely familiar
and each sound
unfolds a tapestry
of stars and jewels

a thousand suns,
galaxies and stars
reside in you

and you glow
with unbearable beauty

I unfold waves of creation within you
that will continue to flow, forevermore.

Inside you, there is endless space, endless love, endless creativity and renewal.

Your life is full of dancing particles, predictable and unpredictable.

We are all petals in the flower of life.

somewhere in this great expanse of atoms is the child you once were

somewhere in this great creation lives every moment ever lived or yet to be

each moment comes from a galaxy far far away but ever so close to you

and I have come to tell you that I am your eternal friend

you may not recognise me in the physical world, but I am everywhere around you

in the trees you walk past in the morning

in everything you see and in the things you do not see

for in everything there is a hidden world

where life is also happening around and within you

life is a hologram of light, even in darkness there is light

for darkness is simply light moving backwards

and as you move the universe also moves,

with each thought and feeling

what is inside you is impossible to describe for life truly is beyond words

we shall meet again sometime, somewhere, somehow
how could we not when life is everywhere

all things exist within all things
as infinite breaths lie dormant within each breath,
all creation lies dormant within each thought,
for creation is the essence which gives life to things
through thought, will or some hidden desire of the soul

all stems from an infinite void,
a fleeting moment in life's dream.

The Divine Nature

A leaf is falling
smiling at the clouds
in total freedom
and trust

The divine nature
holds all in its embrace

In the heart of a bustling city
In the soul of a forest
A glowing ray shines through

A lonely seagull glides over the ocean
While the desert sings it's soulful song

A whisper
a cry
a child is born

and someone sheds a tear of joy

while
somewhere else
someone else
cries tears of sadness

The world goes on turning

The divine nature is present in all things.

everything shall become a living memory in your heart;
nothing, no-one, shall be left behind or forgotten.

in this dream of infinite colour, all is a projection,
a transforming thought in the mind of existence
creating infinite space in each moment
as the universal heart expands and contracts
and love pours forth and recedes
meeting at the intersection of heaven and earth
where spirit morphs into matter
and all and nothing are the same thing
through this breath that breathes all into being
the world keeps turning, our perspective changing
as life melts into death and back into life
through the great ocean of existence
governed by a purpose known only to those who sleep
with eyes open ...

in dreams, our vision is clear but unspeakable,
all that can be said is that each moment holds an eternity,
and our sum is far greater than our parts;
our story continues, guided by the collective will,
swayed by a symphony of atoms,
that merge to form trees, clouds, mountains, oceans,
every atom, a particle of truth

feint atoms of memory
like light from an ancient star
flowing from a primordial void far back in time
when we were but a thought waiting for the first moment
to arrive ... that's how long I have known you

the universe with all its spaces, dimensions, hidden and seen,
is present inside you

Together

in silence, all knowledge is revealed

to an open heart, all wisdom

love remains always

even as the past becomes a fading memory

night comes, the dreamworld opens

and you are here with me

together we explore imaginary worlds

in one another

I reach for the beauty inside you

and touch the infinite absolute light

all that has passed has passed

it will not come again

and yet here we are together

like there is no beginning or end

Through acceptance, we move through life with greater joy.

Surrender your will to the will of the divine spirit,
which, in essence, is you.

fading into the eternal past is the eternal future

one day 'we' will collectively evolve

and be as wise

as trees and flowers

and the love which has always

lived inside our hearts

shall flow out

and fill every atom

of space so densely

that it leaves no room for

misunderstanding

hatred or fear

and our only tears

shall be of bliss and joy

and our only thoughts

of love

You are an ever-evolving thought
in this ever-expanding moment

you appear
as a hologram of light
bursting through the veil of time
filling my heart and mind
with a beautiful familiar thought

beyond this noise, there is a peaceful silence
beyond chaos, perfect order
beyond this world, there is oneness

When the world weeps
it is not the world of nature that weeps
but the human soul

nothing is lacking
for all is part of you
life is always at the centre

Message of Compassion and Oneness

Once in a while, I will come to you as I do now, in this moment in time, in space, in this dream called life, a reflection of all that is and is still to be.

Seeds of God and creation, of goddesses, beings of light, love and pure wisdom, this is what you are.

I wish to talk to you about a quality you can choose to cultivate and nurture to live a happier and more fulfilling life. This quality, dear one, is compassion. But how do you grow and nurture it?

The first step is to understand, to really, truly understand and feel with all your heart that all is one. Energetic currents connect us. Threads of love connect us all. No-one and no-thing are separate. Everything affects everyone, every thought just as much as every action. For thoughts are energy and felt on a subconscious level.

Secondly, have compassion for yourself. Forgive yourself. Be kind and know that nothing and nobody in this world is perfect when judged from a human perspective. Life, in all its mystery, unanswered questions and seeming imperfection, is perfect. One can only see this from a higher perspective. You can feel this through the quiet solitude of your heart.

Accept and be compassionate toward yourself, and you will be better equipped to be compassionate to others. Please do not confuse compassion with self-pity for they are vastly different. Compassion is a form of wisdom and love. It promotes deep understanding and acceptance. In accepting yourself, you can more readily accept others.

Acceptance does not mean things cannot change for the better or that you give up on trying to improve your life or the life of others. Don't stop trying to make the world a better place. Don't give up on your dreams or your passions but pursue them with greater empathy, kindness and love.

Life is a game. As a player, you are here to experience all that your soul has chosen. Grow and expand your awareness and feel the beauty of existence. Life is no small thing. It is fathomless, omnipresent, multidimensional and infinitely so. You are meant to become more, to glow ever brighter through the light of wisdom and become a mirror of your higher self.

Words are so limiting; they are confined to space and time. However, I cannot take you beyond them without confusing you. One can only feel the limitlessness of reality through silence. Words offer signposts and stepping stones, but not a solid path to the Divine.

It is difficult for you to understand that opposing statements and contradictions are aspects of oneness or the one thing. Or, that what you think is wrong and what you believe is right are both valid, both right and wrong, merely aspects of the whole story.

All is one. Let this be your mantra. Repeat this over and over, especially when you experience anything negative or disturbing. This will help you be more compassionate to yourself and others, for we are each integral to the whole. Together we are complete. Feel and be aware of the oneness in your heart and thoughts.

Make this your mantra:

All is one. I am one with all.
I am not better nor worse, higher nor lower.
All is an aspect of the one.